Inspired by
A. A. Milne

Winnie-the-Pooh's Colors

With Decorations by
Ernest H. Shepard

Anytime Books
NEW YORK

Copyright © 1995 by Dutton Children's Books
Coloring of the illustrations copyright © 1992 by Dutton Children's Books
Individual copyrights for illustrations:

Winnie-the-Pooh, copyright © 1926 by E. P. Dutton & Co., Inc.;
copyright renewal 1954 by A. A. Milne.
The House At Pooh Corner, copyright © 1928 by E. P. Dutton & Co., Inc.;
copyright renewal 1956 by A. A. Milne.

All rights reserved.

Published in the United States by Anytime Books,
an imprint of Penguin USA
375 Hudson Street
New York, New York 10014

Designed by Joseph Rutt
Printed in Hong Kong

This book is part of an Anytime Books collection.
It is not intended for individual sale.

Pooh's sweater is red.

Piglet wears a red scarf.

Christopher Robin's front door is green.

Piglet wears a
green sweater.

Pooh floats under a blue balloon.

The sky is blue.

Christopher Robin wears a yellow hat.

The bee is black and yellow.

Piglet picks purple flowers.

Pooh has a purple honey pot.

Tigger is orange.

Pooh and Piglet walk toward an orange sunset.

Rabbit is brown.

Eeyore's house is made of **brown** sticks.

Pooh is gold.

Pooh's honey is gold.

Eeyore is gray.

The heffalump is gray.

Pooh sits in a
pink chair.

The bathtub is pink.

Snow is white.

Christopher Robin wears a *white* shirt.

The umbrella is black.

Christopher Robin's boots are black.